PERFECT AS I AM

MICAH AND MYRAH

BY MAAME SERWAA

Published by Melanin Origins LLC
PO Box 122123; Arlington, TX 76012
Copyright 2018

First Edition
The author asserts the moral right under the Copyright, Designs and Patents Act of 1988 to be identified
as the author of this work.

Library of Congress Control Number: 2018931967

ISBN: 9781626768062 hardback
ISBN: 9781626768000 paperback
ISBN: 9781626768055 ebook

Dedication

To my children Micah and Myrah: you have inspired me in a way I could never imagine and have shown me a love I could never fathom. The world is yours.

I am perfect just as I am.

My hair is full of beauty and magic.

My skin comes from the sun.

I wear an invisible crown.

I keep my head high, because I come from royalty.

My words have power, so I declare that my future is bright.

I trust in myself, and I know that I will always be great.

I am worth far more than diamonds, gold, or any precious stone.

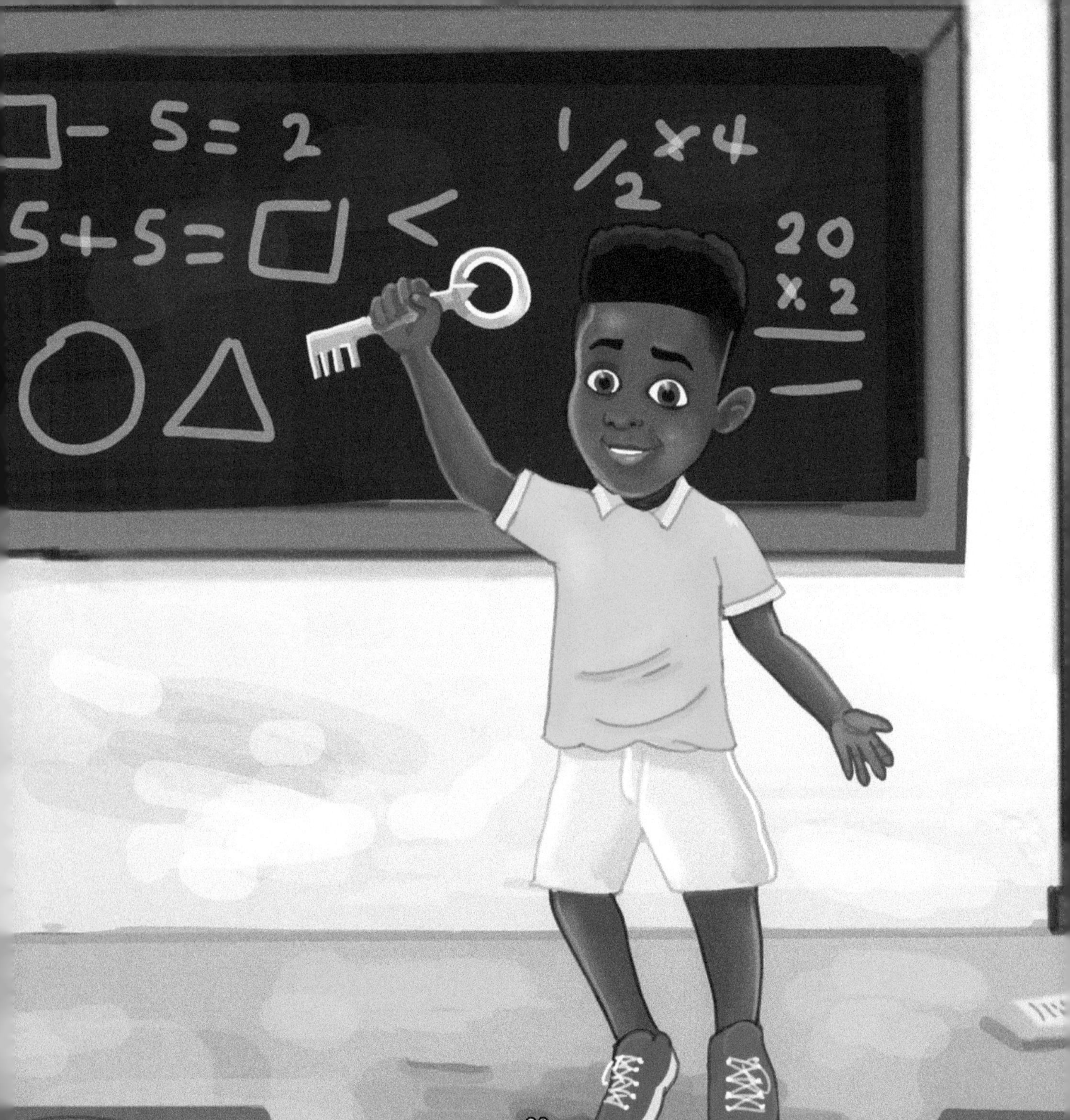
- 5 = 2
5+5 =
<
1/2 x 4
20
x 2

I hold the key to the world in the palm of my hand,

and I know that I can be anything
I want to be when I grow up.

Love is all around me.

Kindness is within me.

I am ready to succeed at whatever I put my mind to, because I am perfect. Perfect just as I am.

CPSIA information can be obtained
at www.ICGtesting.com
Printed in the USA
BVHW020828110321
602010BV00020BA/1660